STEREOPHONICS
LANGUAGE.
SEX.
VIOLENCE.
OTHER?

WISE PUBLICATIONS
part of The Music Sales Group
London / New York / Paris / Sydney / Copenhagen / Berlin / Madrid / Tokyo

Published by
Wise Publications,
8/9 Frith Street, London, W1D 3JB, England.

Exclusive distributors:
Music Sales Limited,
Distribution Centre, Newmarket Road, Bury St Edmunds,
Suffolk, IP33 3YB, England.

Music Sales Pty Limited,
120 Rothschild Avenue, Rosebery,
NSW 2018, Australia.

Order No. AM92025
ISBN 0-7119-4132-7
This book © Copyright 2005 by Wise Publications,
a division of Music Sales Limited.

Music arrangements by Martin Shellard.
Music processed by Paul Ewers Music Design.

Printed in the United Kingdom.

www.musicsales.com

Guitar Tablature Explained 79

SUPERMAN

Words & Music by Kelly Jones

*chords implied by bass

You don't know___ what___ it's been___ like, meet-ing some-one like

you. You don't know what it's been like, meet-ing some-one like

you.

Gtr. 1 tacet

Verse

1. You look like Je - sus on an ae - ro - plane, ya head's a - gainst the win-
2. 3. Su - per - man on an ae - ro - plane, sit - ting next to

Gtr. 2 (3rd time only)

Fig. 4 — — — — — — — — — — — — — — — *3° Gtr. 2 plays Fig.4*

6

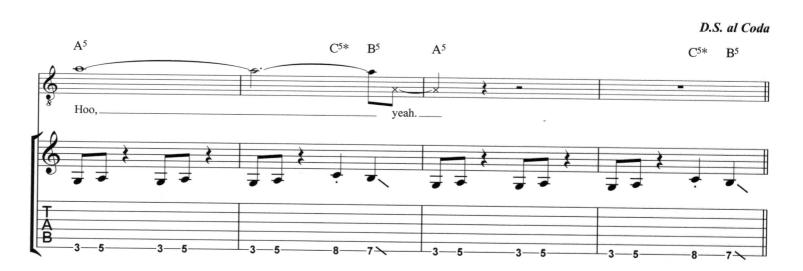

DOORMAN

Words & Music by Kelly Jones

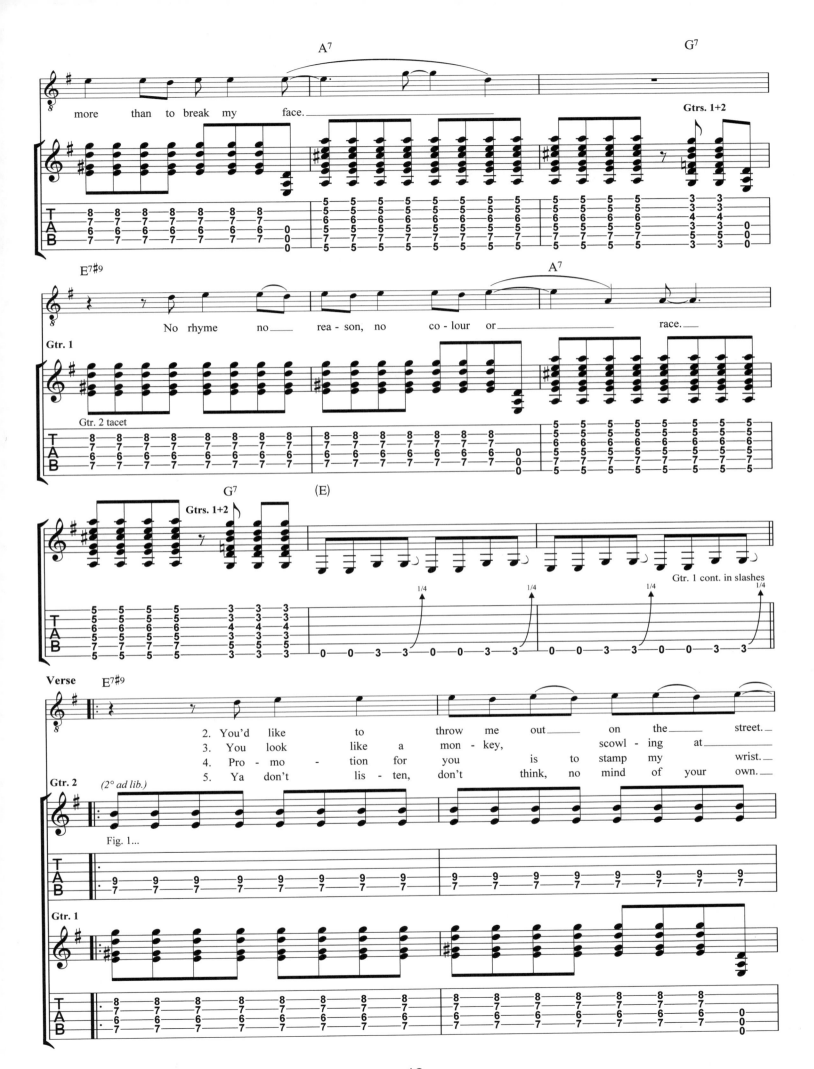

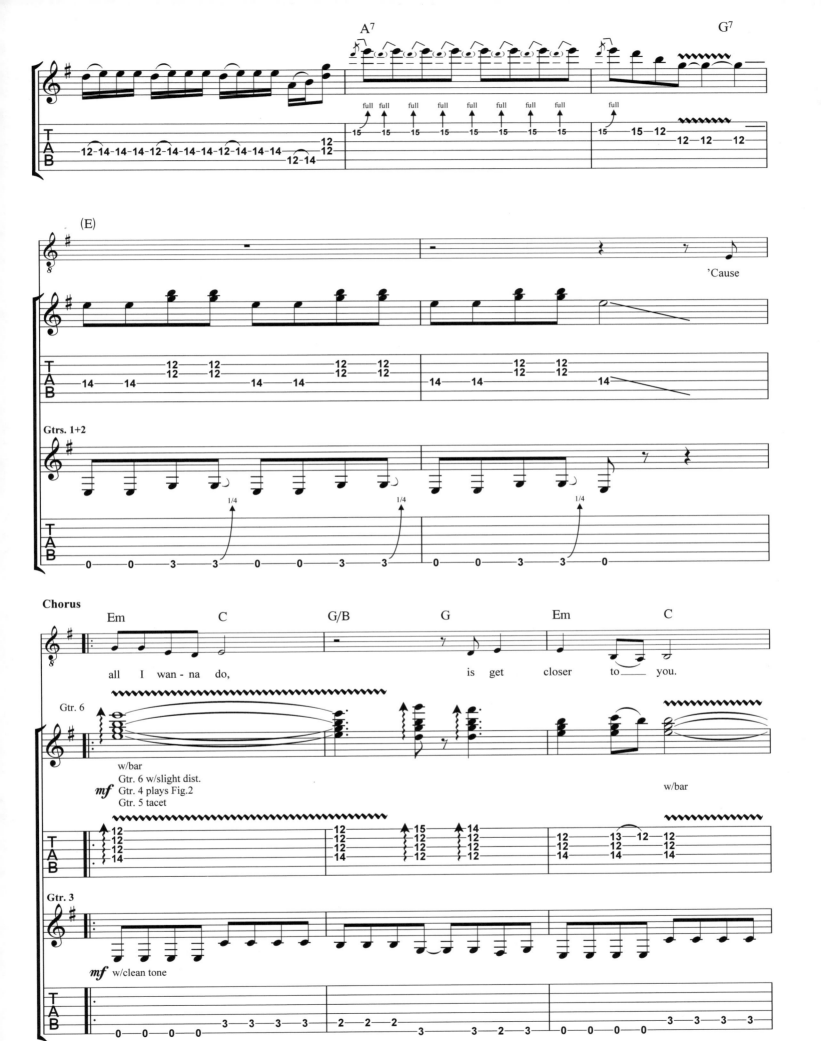

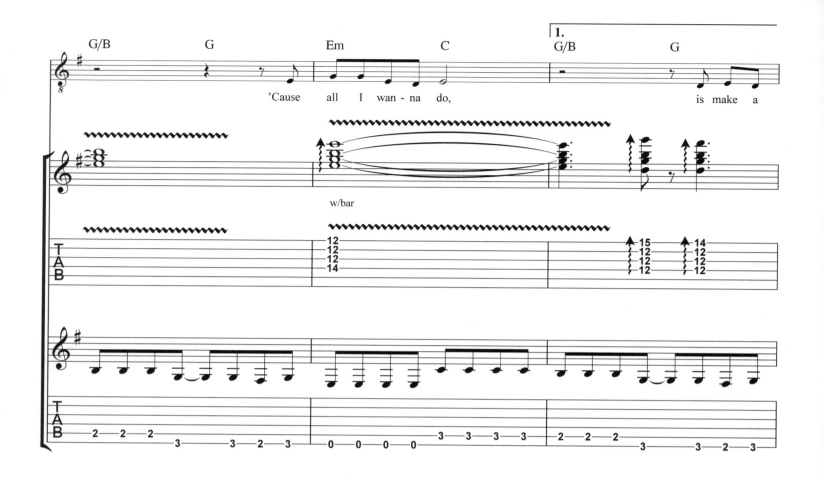

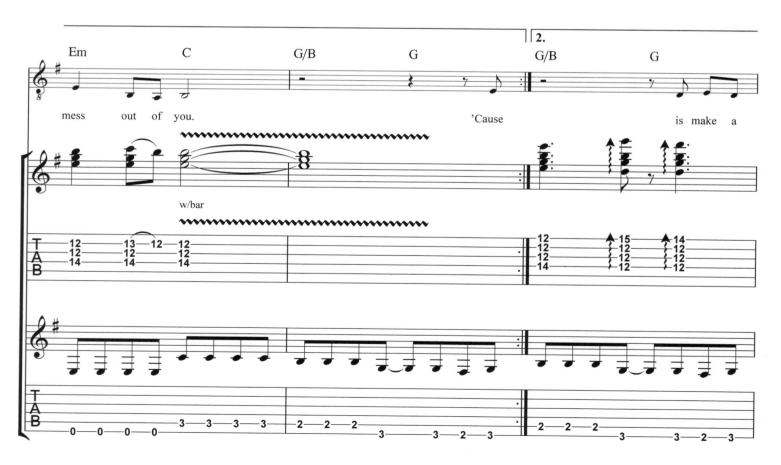

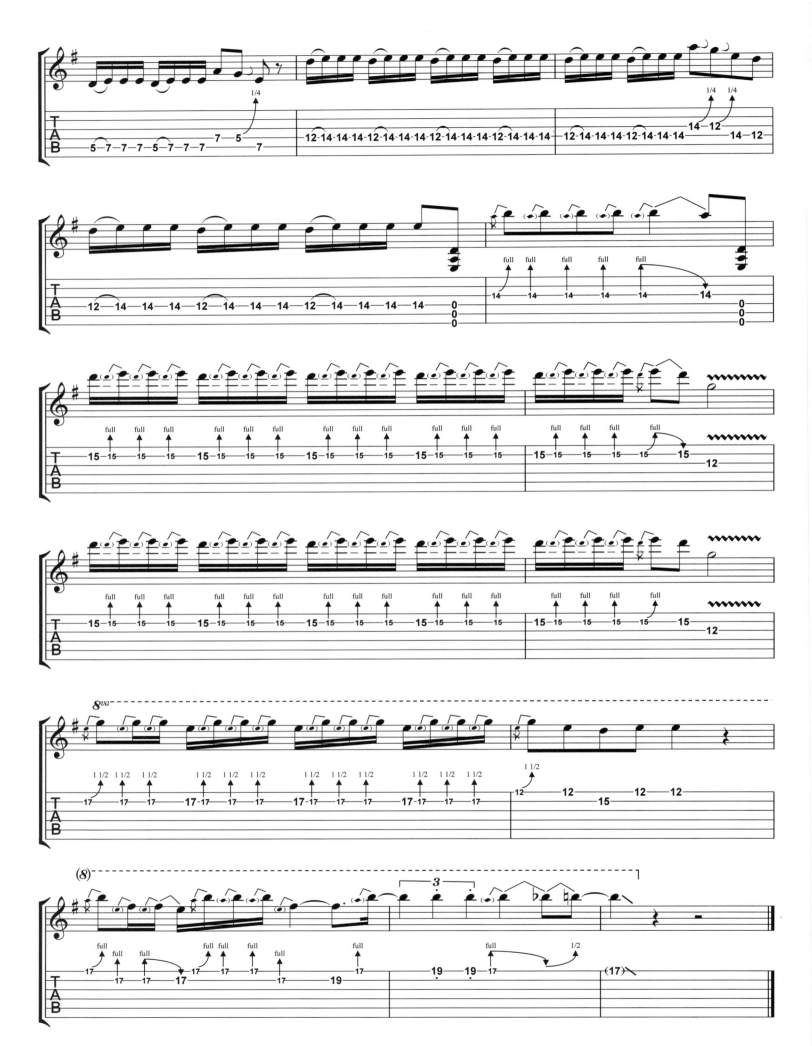

Words & Music by Kelly Jones

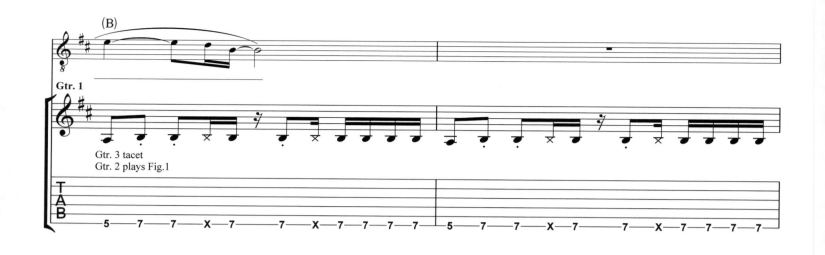

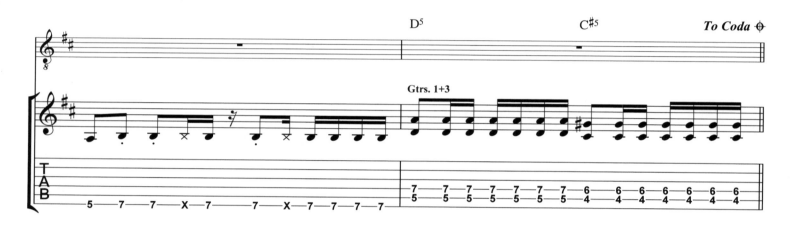

Verse

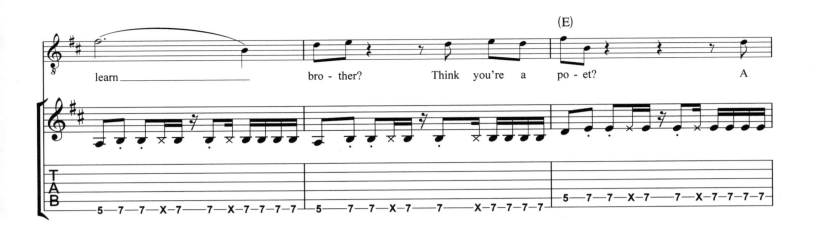

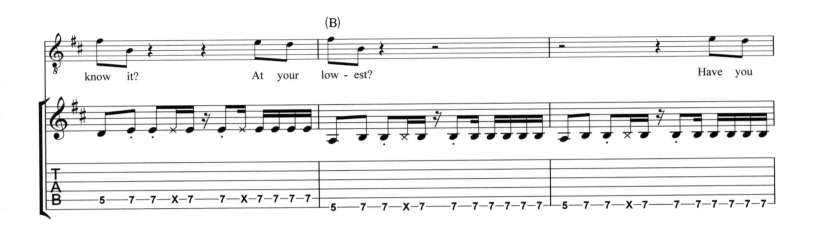

26

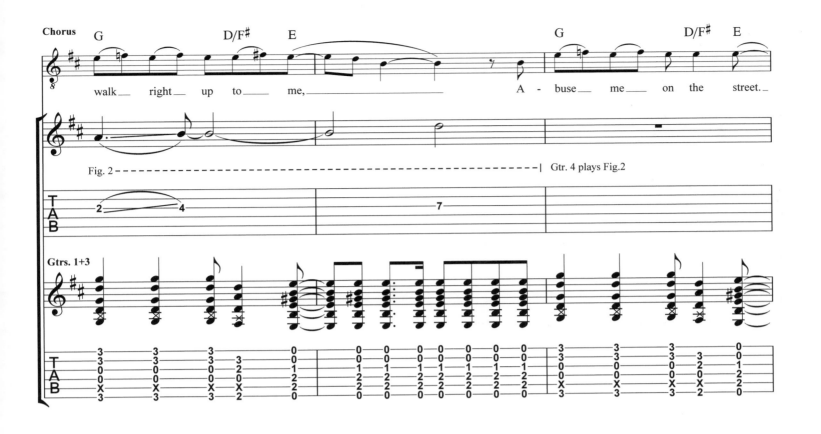

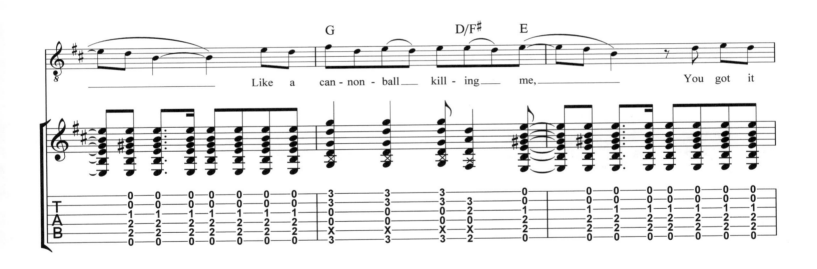

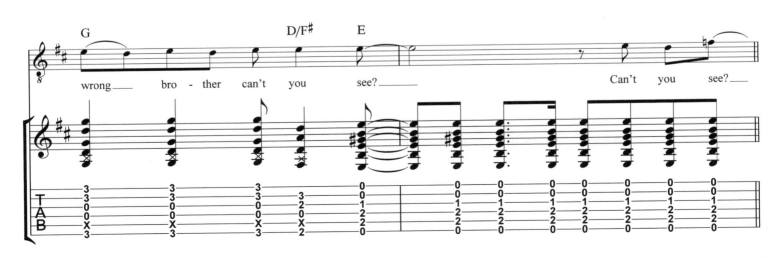

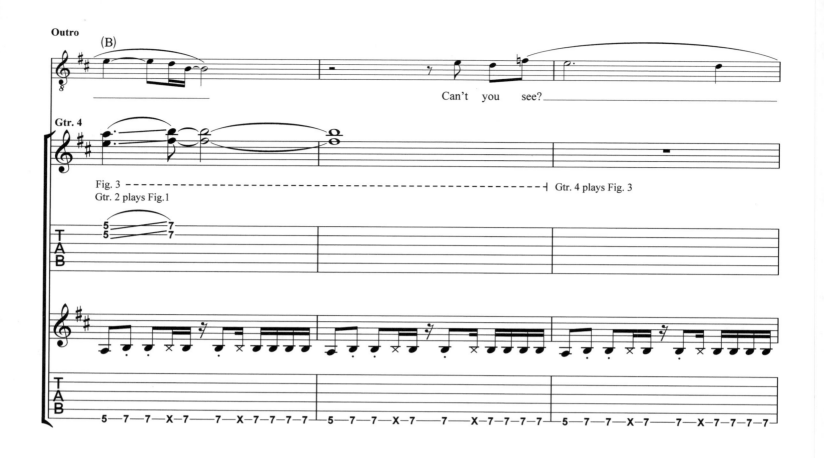

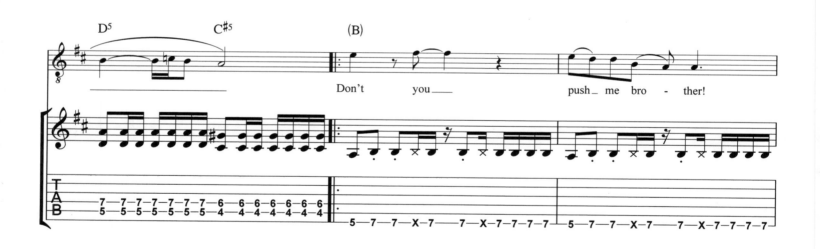

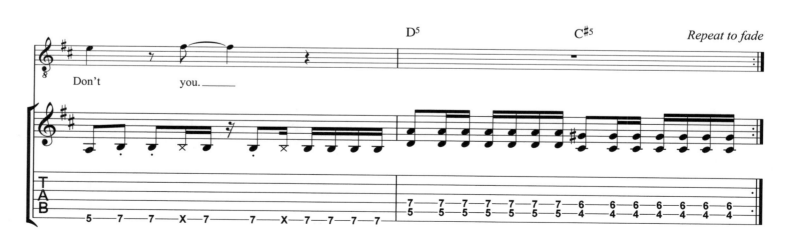

Words & Music by Kelly Jones

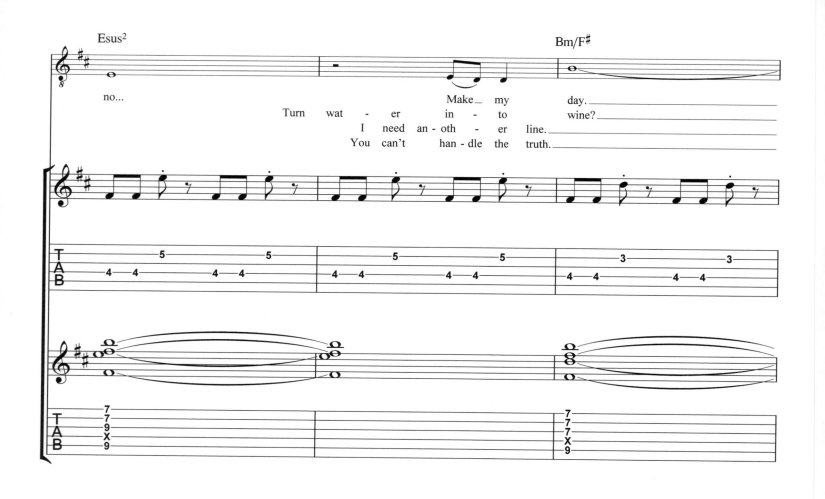

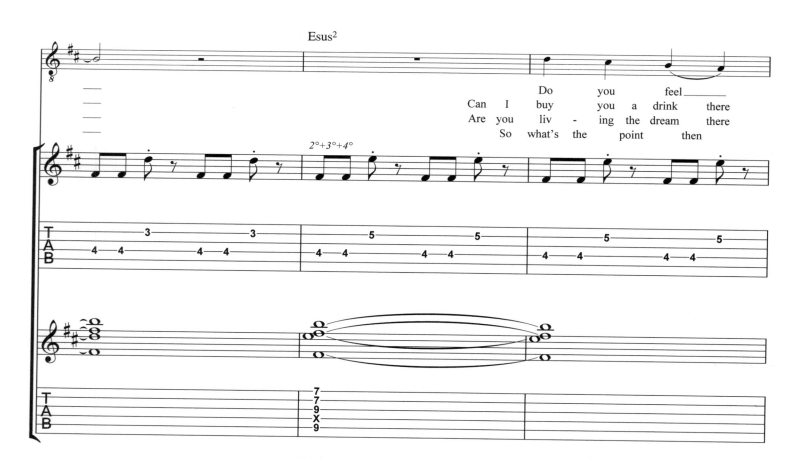

30

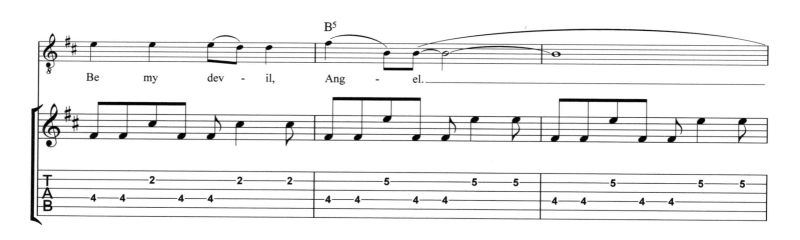

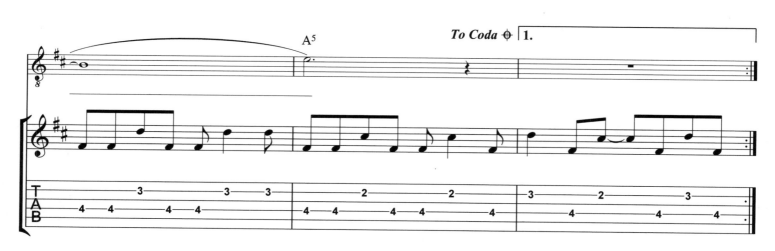

33

DAKOTA

Words & Music by Kelly Jones

...Fig. 1 ends

Verse

1. Think - ing back, think- ing of you. ___
2. Drink - ing back, drink- ing for two. ___
3. Wake - up call, cof - fee and juice. ___

2° Gtr. 1 plays Fig.1

Sum - mer - time think it was June.___ Yeah, think it was June._
Drink - ing with you,___ when drink - ing was new._
Re - mem - ber - ing you,___ what hap - pened to you?_

3° Gtr. 1 plays Fig. 1

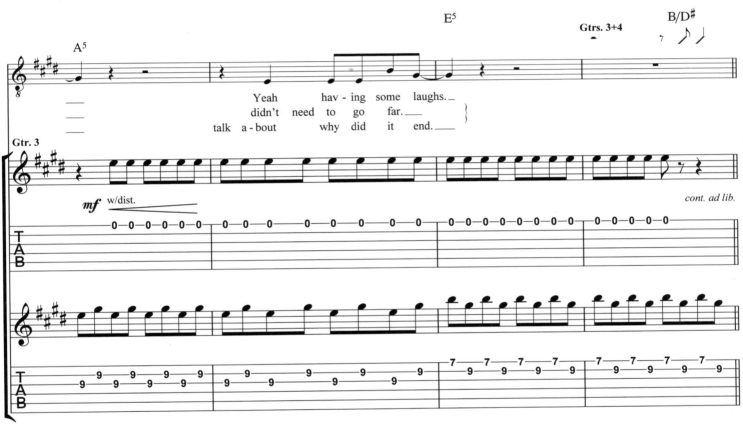

37

39

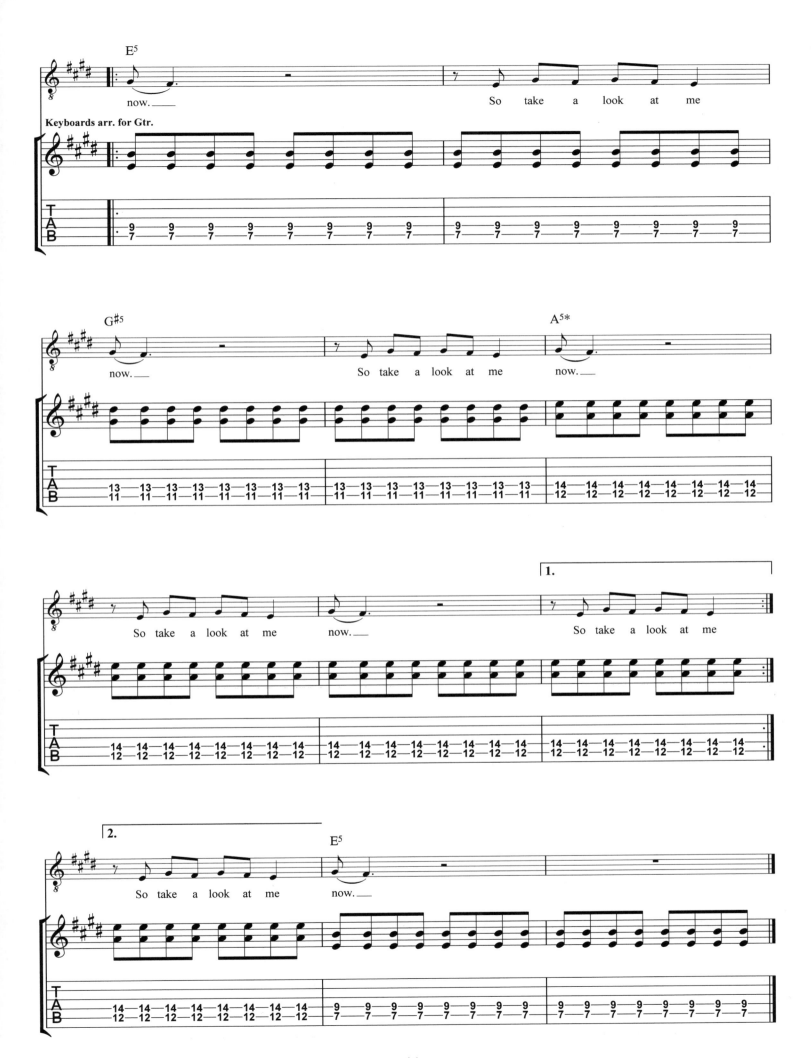

41

REWIND

Words & Music by Kelly Jones

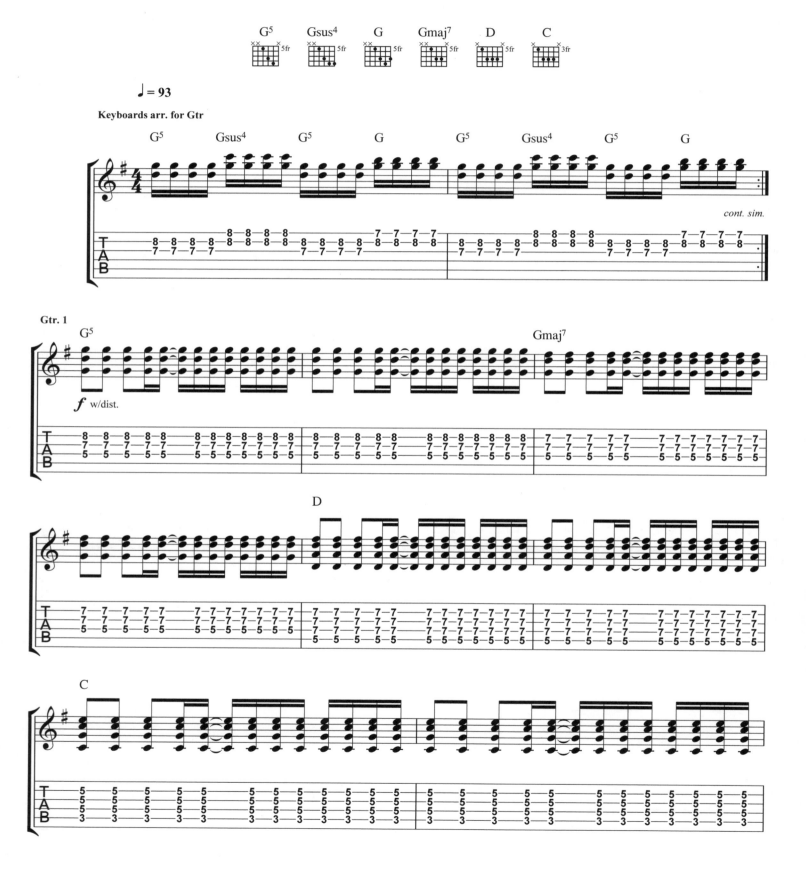

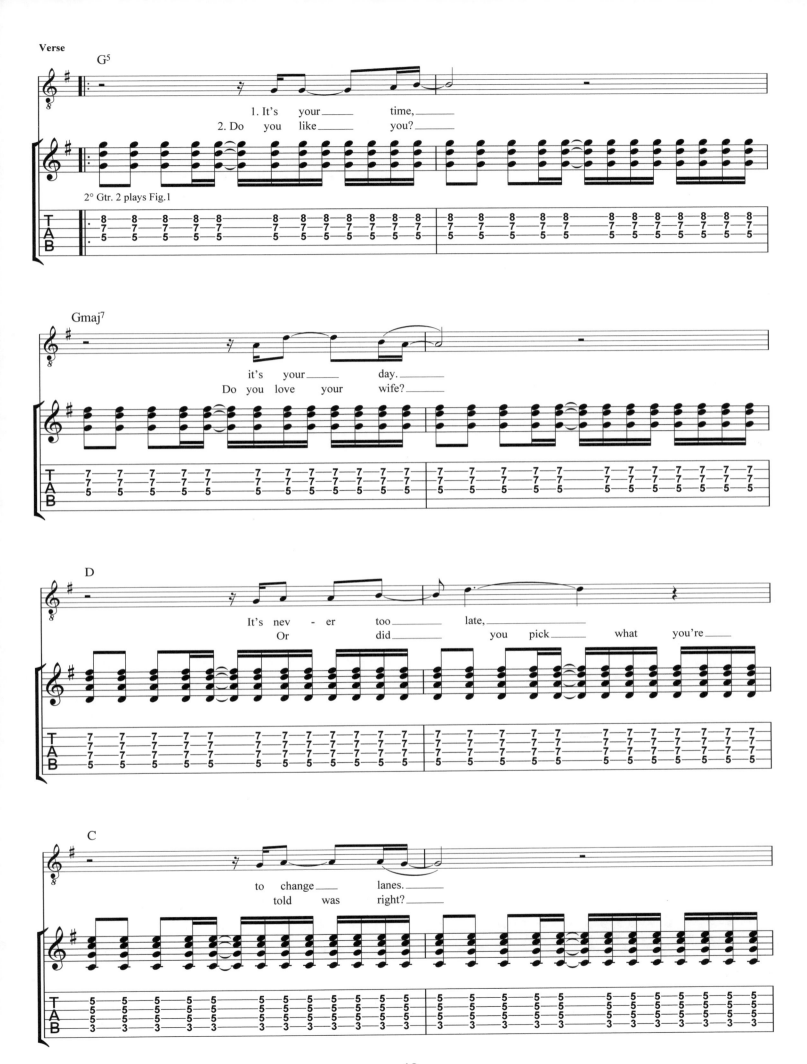

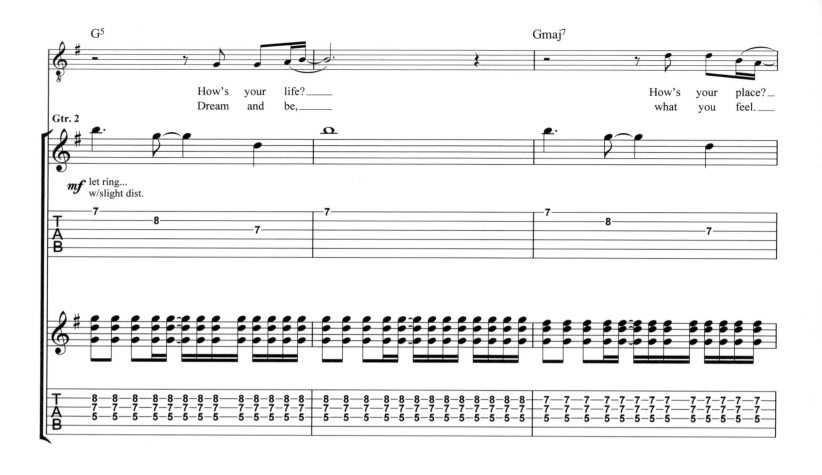

How's your life?_____
Dream and be,_____

How's your place?_____
what you feel._____

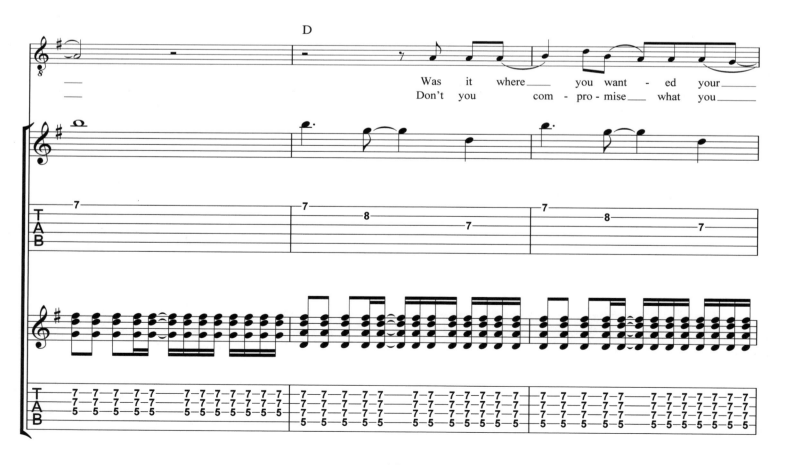

_____ Was it where_____ you want - ed your_____
_____ Don't you com - pro - mise_____ what you

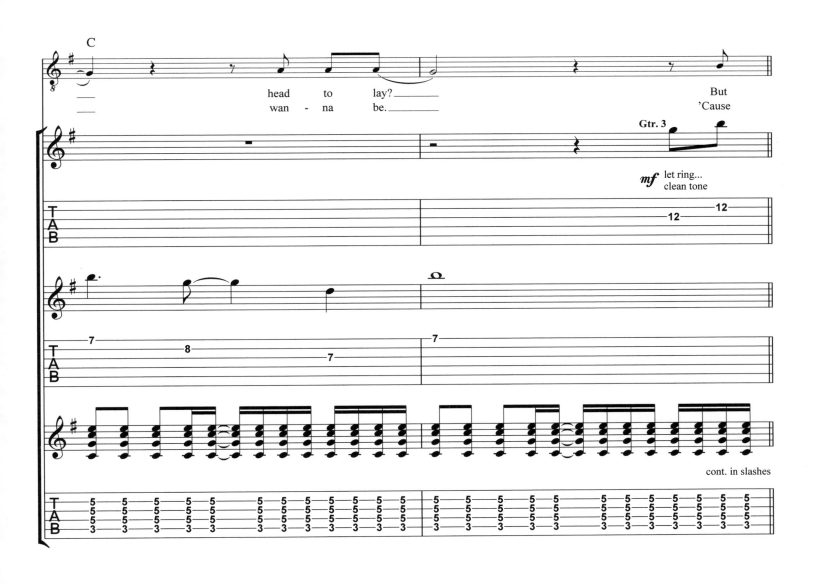

C

head to lay? But
wan - na be. 'Cause

Gtr. 3

mf let ring...
clean tone

cont. in slashes

Pre-chorus

G⁵

cont. sim.

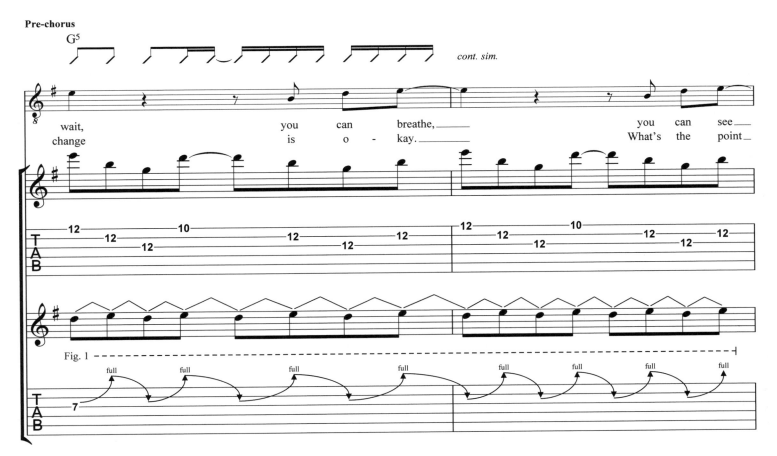

wait, you can breathe, you can see
change is o - kay. What's the point

Fig. 1

full full full full full full full full

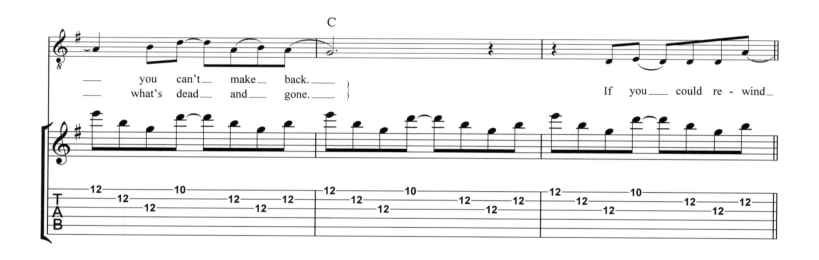

PEDALPUSHER

Words & Music by Kelly Jones

49

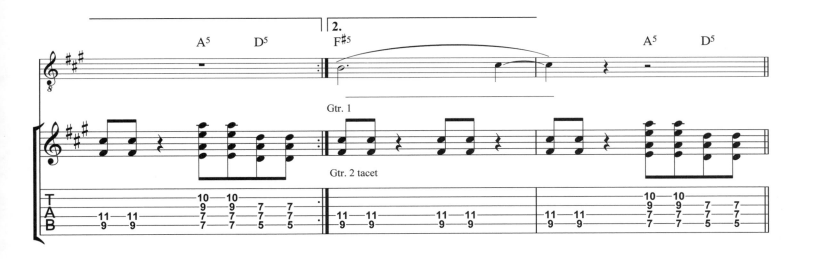

Chorus

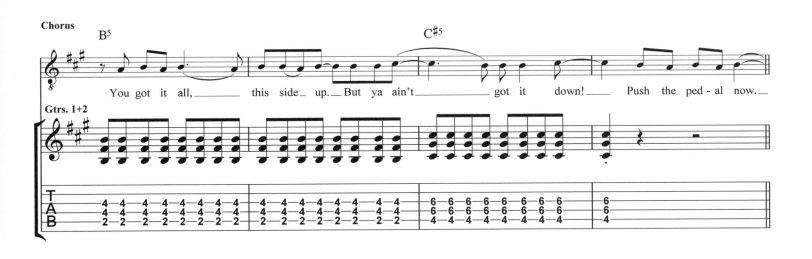

You got it all,_____ this side_ up. But ya ain't_____ got it down!____ Push the ped-al now.__

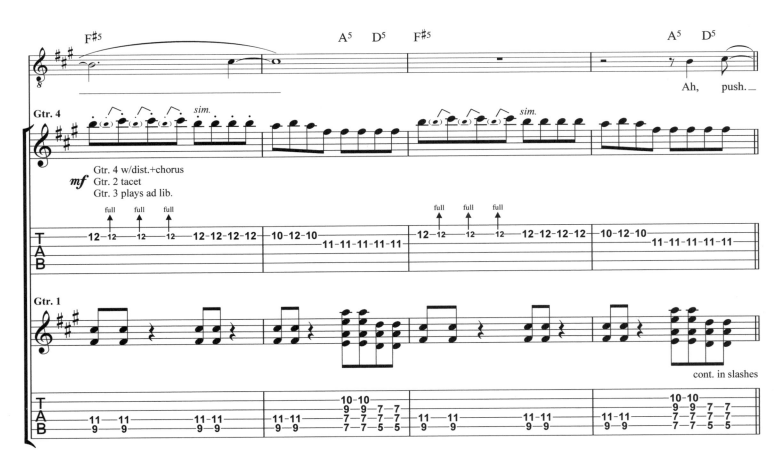

Ah, push.__

Push the ped-al now._____ You got it all,_____ this side___ up.___ But ya ain't_

_____ got it down!___ Push the ped-al now. _____ got it.

Push.

Gtr. 1

Gtr. 2 tacet

G.R.L.

Words & Music by Kelly Jones

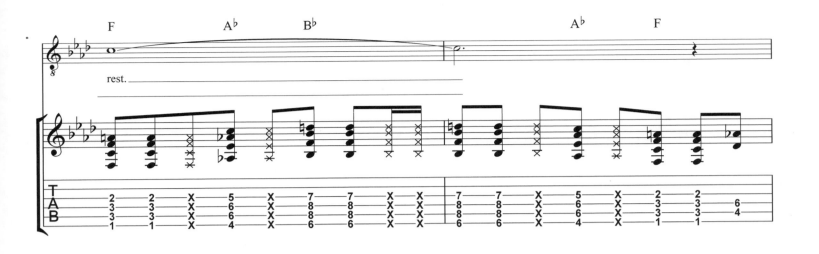

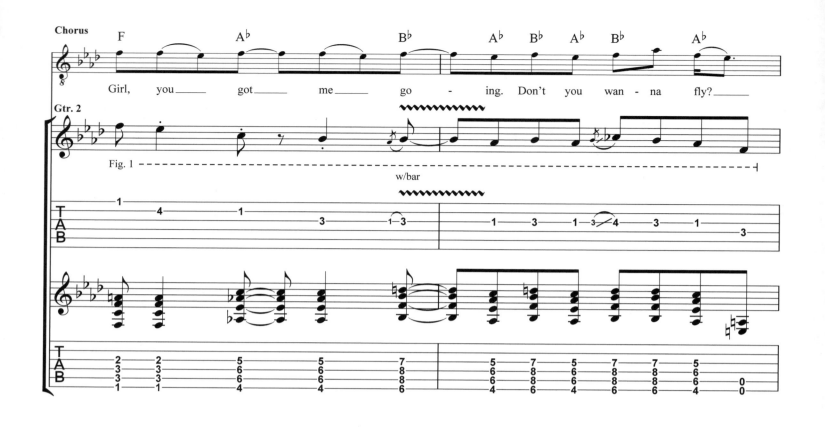

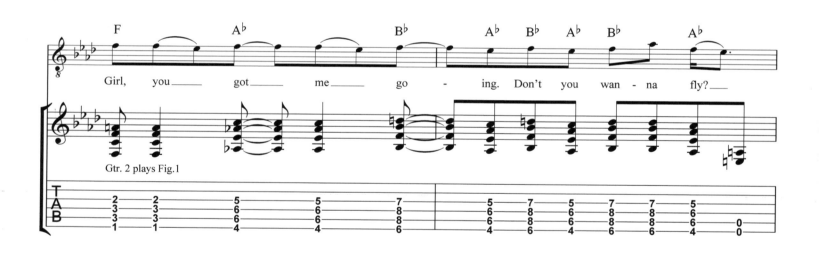

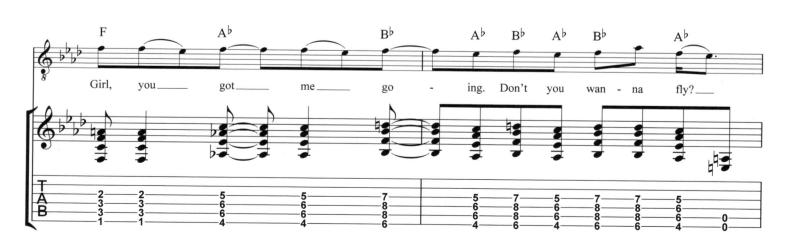

LOLITA

Words & Music by Kelly Jones

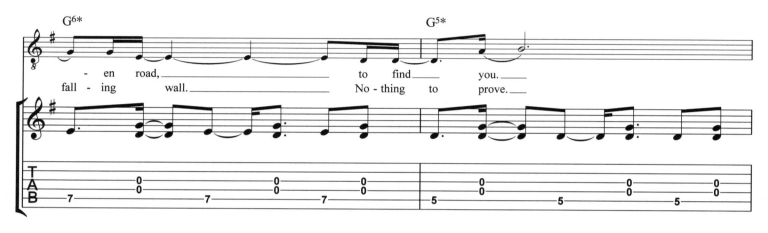

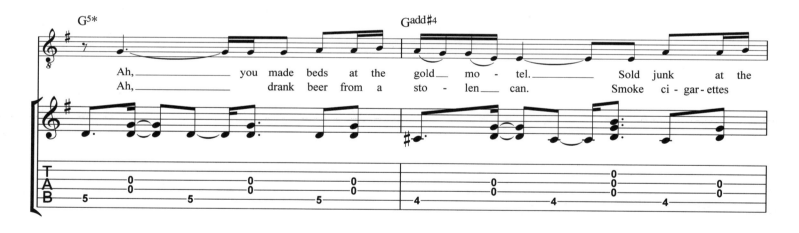

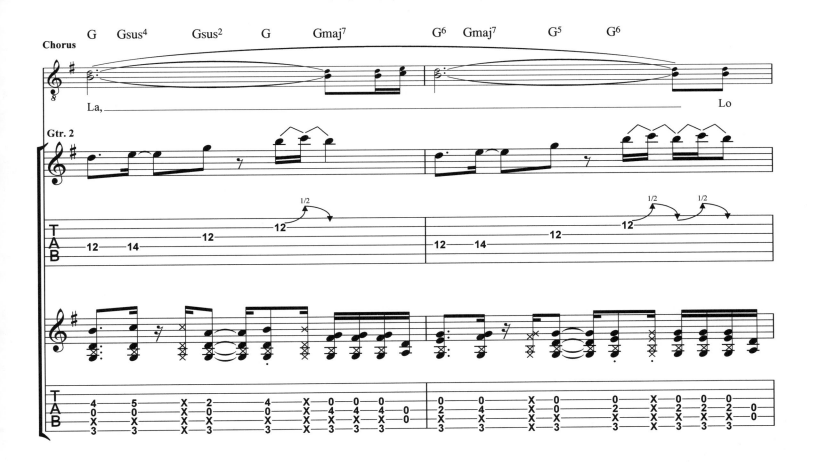

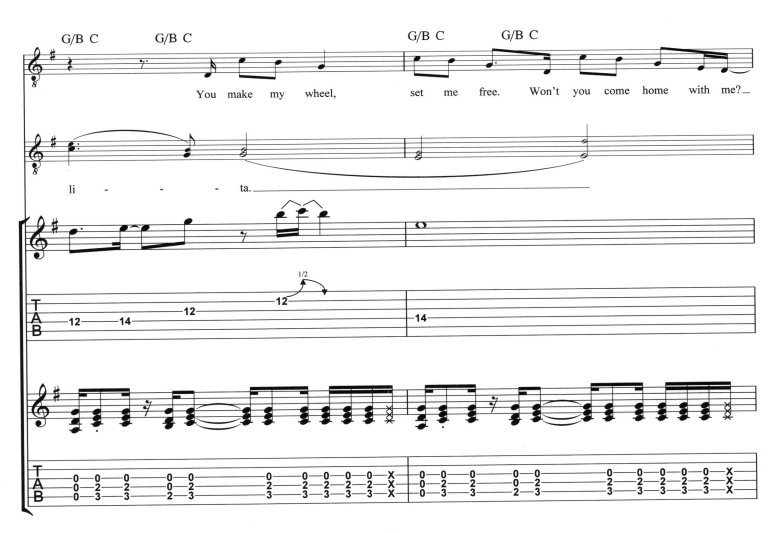

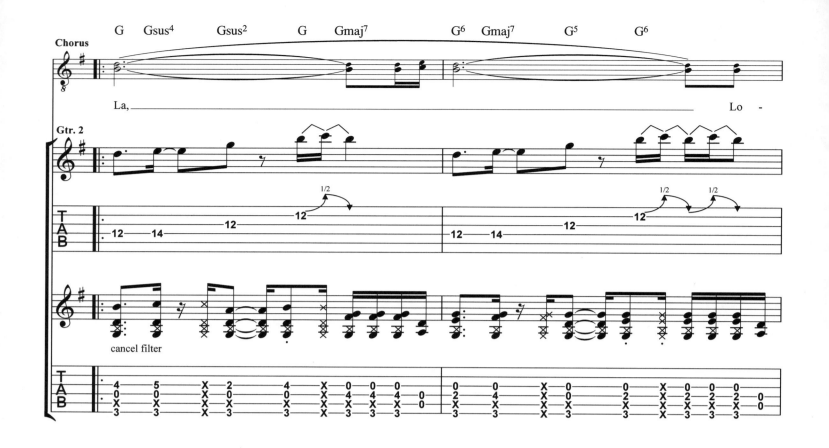

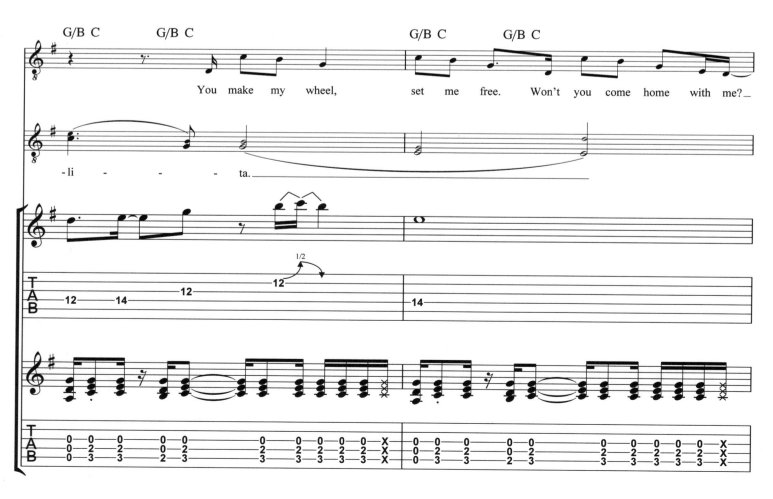

DEADHEAD

Words & Music by Kelly Jones

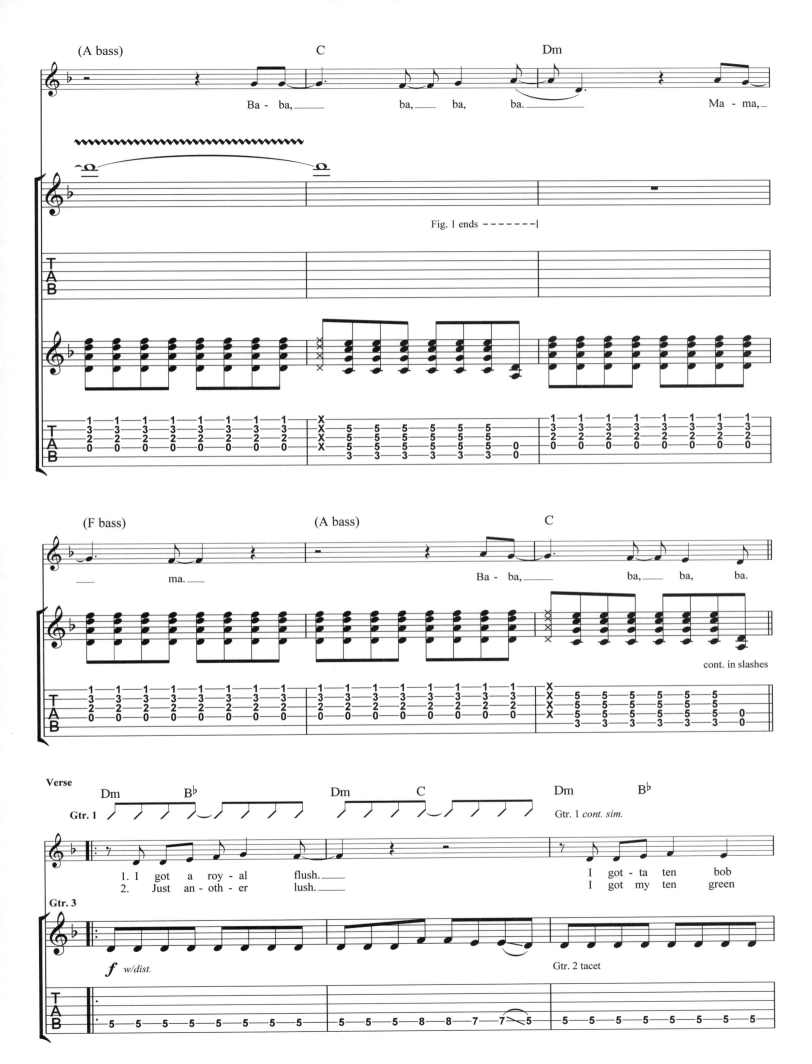

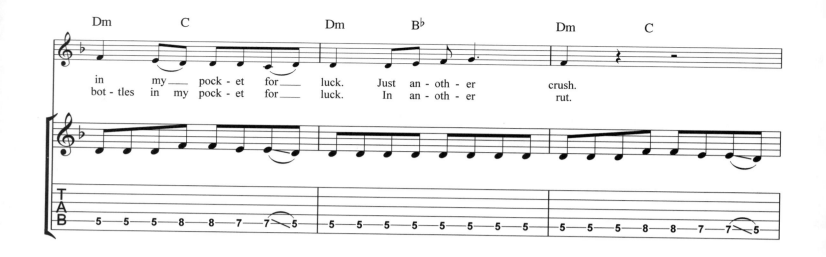

in my ___ pock - et for ___ luck. Just an - oth - er ___ crush.
bot - tles in my pock - et for ___ luck. In an - oth - er ___ rut.

I got my head ___ read ___ in the shed ___ once ___ a - gain, ___
Get your dead - head ___ in the shed ___ once ___ a - gain, ___

Pre - Chorus

Gtrs. 1+3

— my friend. ___
— my friend. ___

Gtr. 1 cont. in slashes

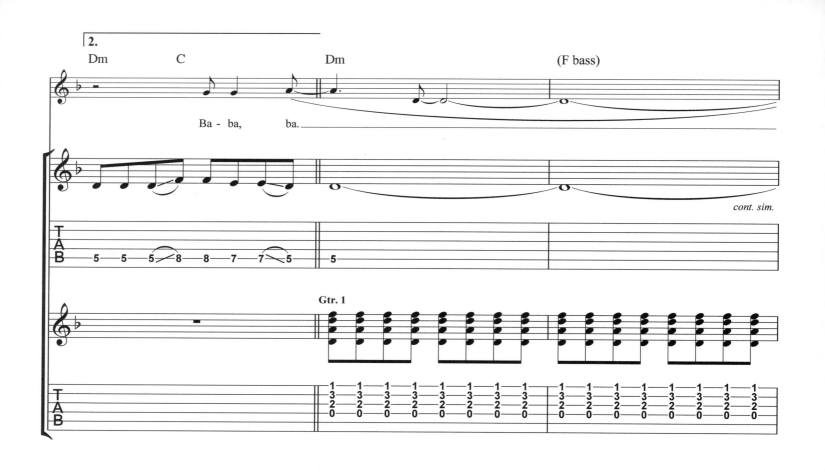

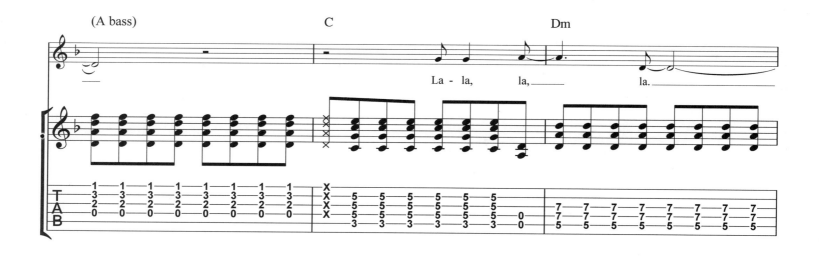

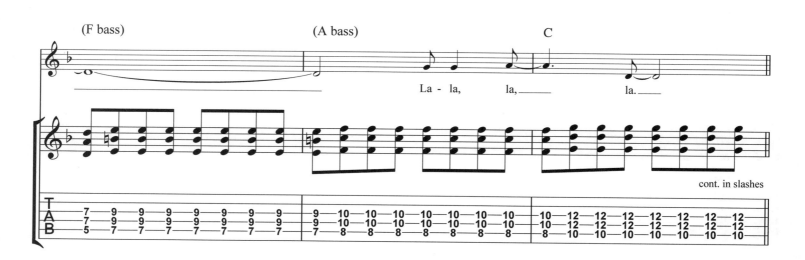

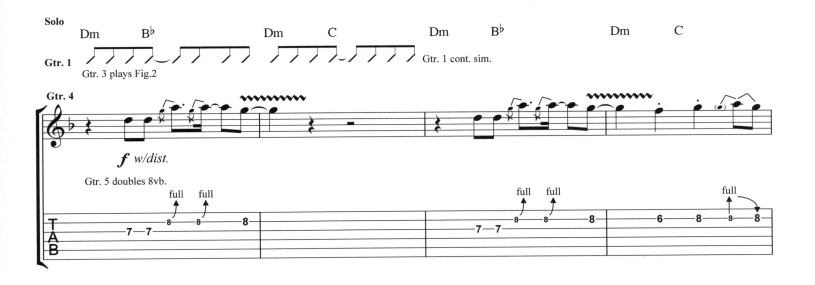

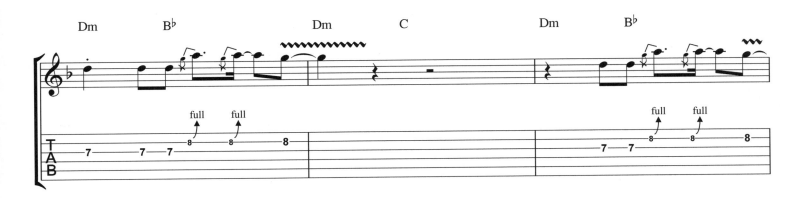

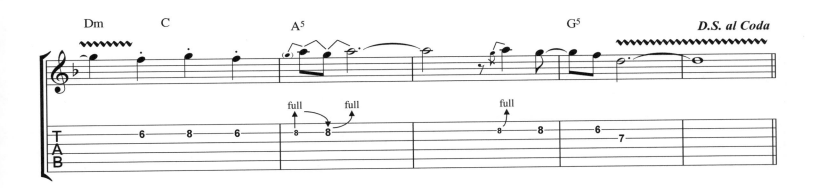

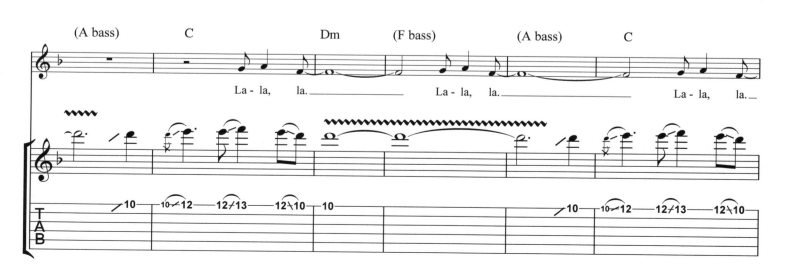

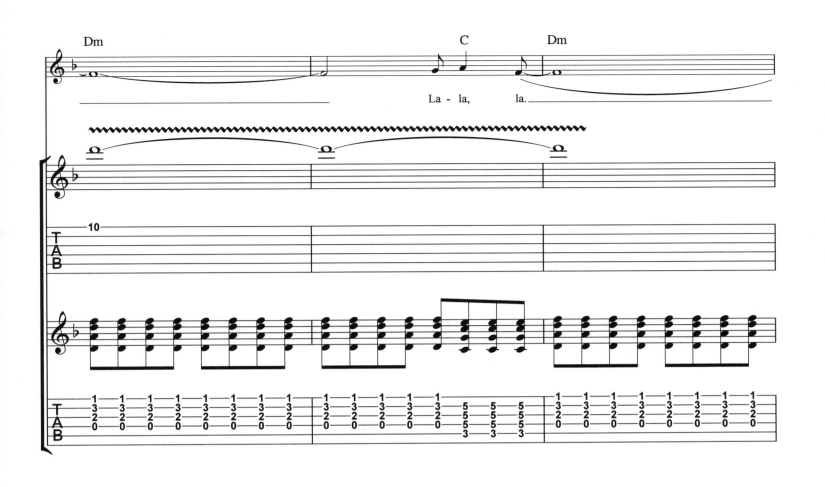

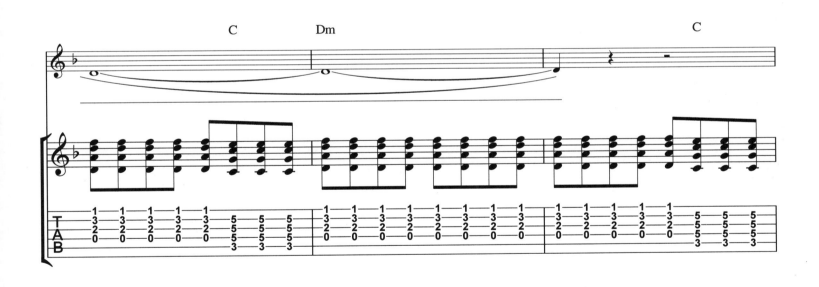

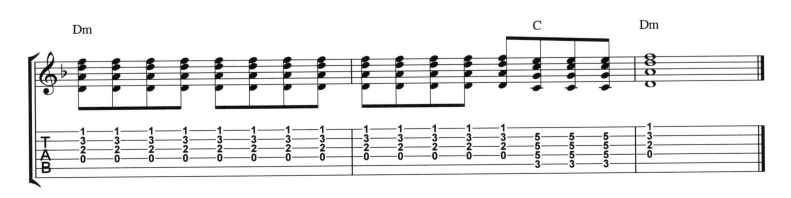

Words & Music by Kelly Jones

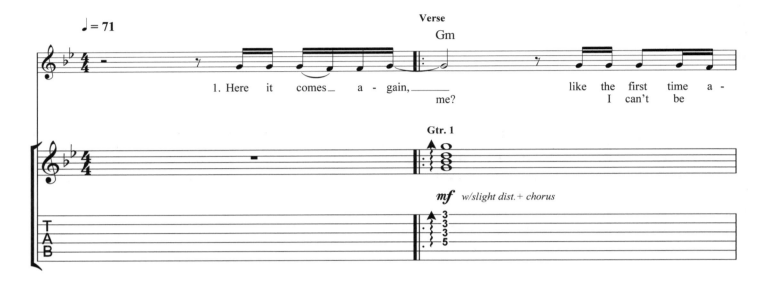

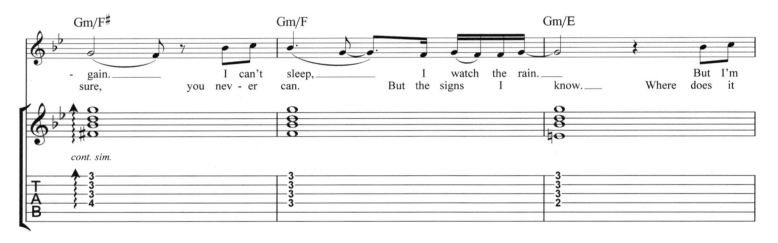

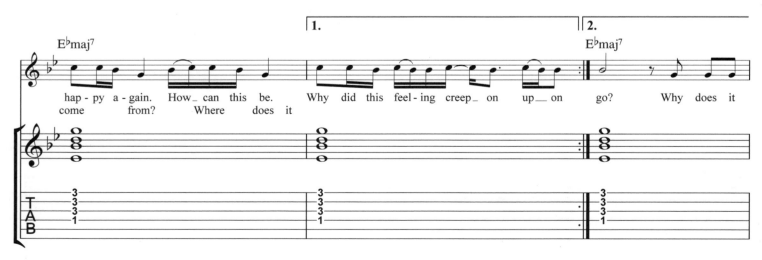

More,_____ more._____

_____ Here it comes a - gain,_____ that feel - ing a - gain.

cont. sim.

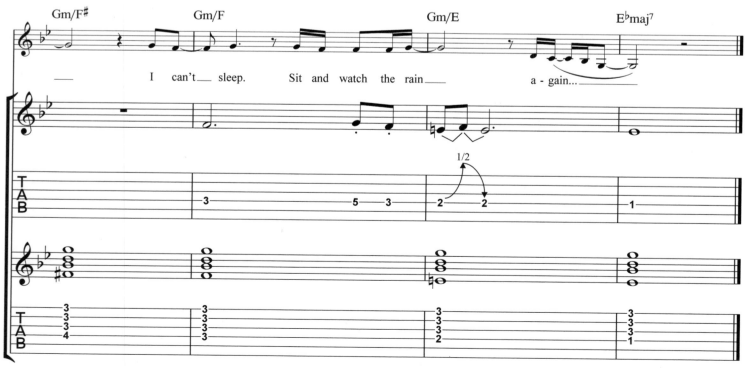

___ I can't__ sleep. Sit and watch the rain___ a - gain..._____

Guitar Tablature Explained

Guitar music can be notated in three different ways: on a musical stave, in tablature, and in rhythm slashes.

RHYTHM SLASHES are written above the stave. Strum chords in the rhythm indicated. Round noteheads indicate single notes.

THE MUSICAL STAVE shows pitches and rhythms and is divided by lines into bars. Pitches are named after the first seven letters of the alphabet.

TABLATURE graphically represents the guitar fingerboard. Each horizontal line represents a string, and each number represents a fret.

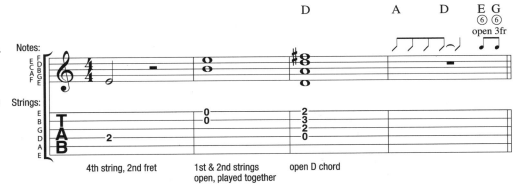

4th string, 2nd fret

1st & 2nd strings open, played together

open D chord

Definitions For Special Guitar Notation

SEMI-TONE BEND: Strike the note and bend up a semi-tone (1/2 step).

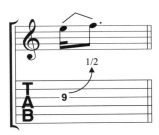

BEND & RELEASE: Strike the note and bend up as indicated, then release back to the original note.

HAMMER-ON: Strike the first note with one finger, then sound the second note (on the same string) with another finger by fretting it without picking.

NATURAL HARMONIC: Strike the note while the fret-hand lightly touches the string directly over the fret indicated.

WHOLE-TONE BEND: Strike the note and bend up a whole-tone (whole step).

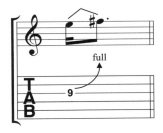

COMPOUND BEND & RELEASE: Strike the note and bend up and down in the rhythm indicated.

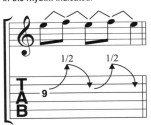

PULL-OFF: Place both fingers on the notes to be sounded, strike the first note and without picking, pull the finger off to sound the second note.

PICK SCRAPE: The edge of the pick is rubbed down (or up) the string, producing a scratchy sound.

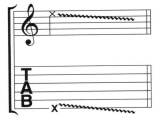

GRACE NOTE BEND: Strike the note and bend as indicated. Play the first note as quickly as possible.

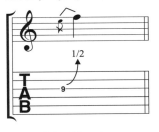

PRE-BEND: Bend the note as indicated, then strike it.

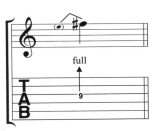

LEGATO SLIDE (GLISS): Strike the first note and then slide the same fret-hand finger up or down to the second note. The second note is not struck.

PALM MUTING: The note is partially muted by the pick hand lightly touching the string(s) just before the bridge.

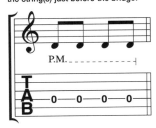

QUARTER-TONE BEND: Strike the note and bend up a 1/4 step.

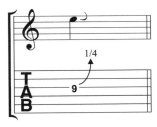

PRE-BEND & RELEASE: Bend the note as indicated. Strike it and release the note back to the original pitch.

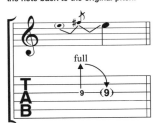

MUFFLED STRINGS: A percussive sound is produced by laying the fret hand across the string(s) without depressing, and striking them with the pick hand.

SHIFT SLIDE (GLISS & RESTRIKE): Same as legato slide, except the second note is struck.

NOTE: The speed of any bend is indicated by the music notation and tempo.